Grade 3 Violin

Improve your sight-reading!

Paul Harris

Extra Stage: Revision available to download from
fabermusicstore.com

The golden rules

A sight-reading checklist

Before you begin to play a piece at sight, always consider the following:

1 Look at the piece for about half a minute and try to feel that you are *understanding* what you see (just like reading these words).

2 Look at the time signature and decide how you will count the piece.

3 Look at the key signature and think about how to finger the notes.

4 Notice patterns – especially those that repeat, or are based on scales and arpeggios.

5 Notice any markings that will help you convey the character.

6 Don't begin until you think you are going to play the piece accurately.

7 Count at least one bar in.

When performing a sight-reading piece

1 Keep feeling the pulse.

2 Keep going at a steady tempo.

3 Remember the finger pattern of the key you are in.

4 Ignore mistakes.

5 Look ahead – at least to the next note.

6 Play musically, always trying to convey the character of the music.

With many thanks to Gillian Secret for her invaluable help.

© 2011 by Faber Music Ltd
This edition first published in 2011 by Faber Music Ltd.
Bloomsbury House 74–77 Great Russell Street London WC1B 3DA
Music processed by Donald Thomson
Cover and page design by Susan Clarke
Cover illustration by Drew Hillier
Printed in England by Caligraving Ltd
All rights reserved

ISBN10: 0-571-53623-9
EAN13: 978-0-571-53623-8

US editions:
ISBN10: 0-571-53663-8
EAN13: 978-0-571-53663-4

To buy Faber Music publications or to find out about the full range of titles available
please contact your local music retailer or Faber Music sales enquiries:
Faber Music Ltd, Burnt Mill, Elizabeth Way, Harlow CM20 2HX
Tel: +44 (0) 1279 82 89 82   Fax: +44 (0) 1279 82 89 83
sales@fabermusic.com   fabermusicstore.com

Introduction

Being a good sight-reader is so important and it's not difficult at all! If you work through this book carefully – always making sure that you really understand each exercise before you play it, you'll never have problems learning new pieces or doing well at sight-reading in exams!

Using the workbook

1 Rhythmic exercises

Make sure you have grasped these fully before you go on to the melodic exercises: it is vital that you really know how the rhythms work. There are a number of ways to do the exercises – see *Improve your sight-reading* Grade 1 for more details.

2 Melodic exercises

These exercises use just the notes (and rhythms) for the Stage, and are organised into Sets which progress gradually. If you want to sight-read fluently and accurately, get into the simple habit of working through each exercise in the following ways before you begin to play it:

- Make sure you understand the rhythm and counting. Clap the exercise through.
- Know what notes you are going to play and the fingering you are going to use.
- Try to hear the piece through in your head. Always play the first note to help.

3 Prepared pieces

Work your way through the questions first, as these will help you to think about or 'prepare' the piece. Don't begin playing until you are pretty sure you know exactly how the piece goes.

4 Going solo!

It is now up to you to discover the clues in this series of practice pieces. Give yourself about a minute and do your best to understand the piece before you play. Check the rhythms and fingering, and try to hear the piece in your head.

Always remember to feel the pulse and to keep going steadily once you've begun. Good luck and happy sight-reading!

Terminology:
Bar = measure

Stage 1

Rhythmic exercises

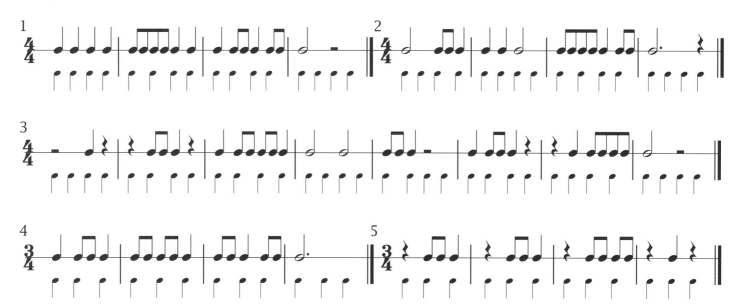

Melodic exercises

Always play the scale and arpeggio
of the key before you begin.

Set 1: Exploring C major

Set 2: Exploring A minor

Prepared pieces

> 1 What is the key of this piece? Play the scale and arpeggio energetically.
>
> 2 Can you spot any repeated 2-bar patterns?
>
> 3 Think through the fingering of the whole piece.
>
> 4 What will you count? Tap the pulse and think the rhythm, then tap the rhythm and think the pulse.
>
> 5 Play the first note and hear the piece through in your head.

1

> 1 In which key is this piece? Play the scale and arpeggio in an agitated style.
>
> 2 What are the similarities and differences between the two 4-bar phrases?
>
> 3 Tap the pulse with your foot and the rhythm with your hands.
>
> 4 Think about how you'll control the bow speed through the piece.
>
> 5 How will you put character into your performance?

2

Improvising

1

Make up your own piece (it can be as long or as short as you like), beginning with this pattern. Keep the pulse steady. Decide on a mood or character before you begin.

2

Now make up your own piece in C major or A minor – using any patterns you like.

Going solo!

Don't forget to prepare each piece carefully before you play it.

Stage 2

Rhythmic exercises

Feel the tied notes strongly, but don't play them.

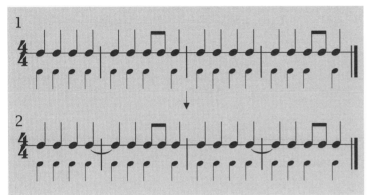 

Melodic exercises

Set 1: Exploring F major

Set 2: Exploring D minor

Prepared pieces

1 What is the key of this piece? Play the scale and arpeggio sadly.

2 Can you spot any scale or arpeggio patterns?

3 Find the ties. Now compare bars 1 and 2 with bars 3 and 4.

4 What will you count? Tap the pulse and think the rhythm, then tap the rhythm and think the pulse.

5 Play the first note and hear the piece through in your head, including dynamics.

1 In which key is this piece? Play the scale and arpeggio rhythmically.

2 How many repeated ideas can you find?

3 Find the tied notes, then tap the pulse with your foot and the rhythm with your hands.

4 Think through the fingering.

5 How will you put character into your performance?

Improvising

Make up your own piece (it can be as long or as short as you like), beginning with this pattern. Keep the pulse steady. Decide on a mood or character before you begin.

Now make up your own piece in F major or D minor – using any notes of the scale you like.

Going solo!

Don't forget to prepare each piece carefully before you play it.

Stage 3

Bb major and
G minor
More ties

Rhythmic exercises

Melodic exercises

Set 1: Exploring Bb major

How are Bb major and
G minor connected?

Set 2: Exploring G minor

Prepared pieces

1   What is the key of this piece? Play the scale and arpeggio cheerfully.

2   Are there any patterns which don't belong to the scale or arpeggio?

3   Find the two ties. Think carefully how you will count them. Tap bars 2 and 3 and 6 and 7 without the ties, then with them.

4   What will you count? Tap the pulse and think the rhythm, then tap the rhythm and think the pulse.

5   Play the first note and hear the piece through in your head, including dynamics.

1   In which key is this piece? Play the scale and arpeggio in a tranquil style.

2   How many bars are based on scale patterns?

3   Think through the fingering.

4   Tap the pulse with one hand and the rhythm with the other. Repeat, swopping hands.

5   What gives you clues to the character of this piece?

Improvising

Make up your own piece (it can be as long or as short as you like), beginning with this pattern. Keep the pulse steady. Decide on a mood or character before you begin.

Now make up your own piece in B♭ major or G minor, using any patterns you like.

Going solo! Don't forget to prepare each piece carefully before you play it.

Paul Harris' Exam Workout

Improve your sight-reading!

New editions

The ability to sight-read fluently is an important part of musical training, whether intending to play professionally, or simply for enjoyment. By becoming a good sight-reader, the player will be able to learn pieces more quickly, pianists will accompany more easily and all musicians will play duets and chamber music with confidence and assurance. Also, in grade examinations, a good performance in the sight-reading test will result in useful extra marks!

These completely new editions are designed to help incorporate sight-reading regularly into practice and lessons, and to prepare for the sight-reading test in grade examinations. They offer a progressive series of enjoyable and stimulating stages which, with careful work, should result in considerable improvement from week to week.

Step by step, the player is encouraged to build up a complete picture of each piece. Rhythmic exercises help develop and maintain a steady beat, whilst melodic exercises assist in the recognition of melodic shapes at a glance. The study of a prepared piece with associated questions for the student to answer helps consolidate acquired skills and, finally, a series of real, unprepared sight-reading tests in *Going Solo*.

Now available: two *Improve Your Sight-reading!* Piano duet books which give players a chance to practise their sight-reading skills with another player. Carefully paced to be used alongside the rest of the series.

ABRSM Editions

0-571-53300-0	Piano Pre-Grade 1
0-571-53301-9	Piano Grade 1
0-571-53302-7	Piano Grade 2
0-571-53303-5	Piano Grade 3
0-571-53304-3	Piano Grade 4
0-571-53305-1	Piano Grade 5
0-571-53306-X	Piano Grade 6
0-571-53307-8	Piano Grade 7
0-571-53308-6	Piano Grade 8
0-571-52405-2	Duets Grades 0–1
0-571-52406-0	Duets Grades 2–3

Trinity Editions

0-571-53750-2	Piano Grade Initial
0-571-53751-0	Piano Grade 1
0-571-53752-9	Piano Grade 2
0-571-53753-7	Piano Grade 3
0-571-53754-5	Piano Grade 4
0-571-53755-3	Piano Grade 5
0-571-53825-8	Electronic Keyboard Initial–Grade 1
0-571-53826-6	Electronic Keyboard Grades 2–3
0-571-53827-4	Electronic Keyboard Grades 4–5

FABER *ff* MUSIC

0-571-53621-2 Violin Grade 1
0-571-53622-0 Violin Grade 2
0-571-53623-9 Violin Grade 3
0-571-53624-7 Violin Grade 4
0-571-53625-5 Violin Grade 5
0-571-53626-3 Violin Grade 6
0-571-53627-1 Violin Grades 7–8

0-571-53699-9 Viola Grades 1–5

0-571-53697-2 Cello Grades 1–3
0-571-53698-0 Cello Grades 4–5

0-571-53700-6 Double Bass Grades 1–5

0-571-51373-5 Descant Recorder Grades 1–3

0-571-51466-9 Flute Grades 1–3
0-571-51467-7 Flute Grades 4–5
0-571-51789-7 Flute Grade 6
0-571-51790-0 Flute Grades 7–8

0-571-51464-2 Clarinet Grades 1–3
0-571-51465-0 Clarinet Grades 4–5
0-571-51787-0 Clarinet Grade 6
0-571-51788-9 Clarinet Grades 7–8

0-571-51635-1 Saxophone Grades 1–3
0-571-51636-X Saxophone Grades 4–5

0-571-51633-5 Oboe Grades 1–3
0-571-57021-6 Oboe Grades 4–5

0-571-51148-1 Bassoon Grades 1–5

0-571-51076-0 Horn Grades 1–5

0-571-50989-4 Trumpet Grades 1–5
0-571-51152-X Trumpet Grades 5–8

0-571-56860-2 Trombone Grades 1–5

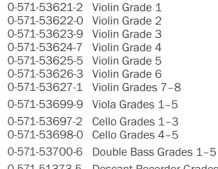

Improve your aural!

New editions

The very thought of aural, especially in examinations, strikes fear into the heart of many young pianists and instrumentalists. But aural should not be an occasional optional extra – it's something to be developing all the time, because having a good ear will help improve musicianship more than any other single musical skill.

Improve your aural! is designed to take the fear out of aural. Through fun listening activities, boxes to fill in and practice exercises, these workbooks and CDs focus on all the elements of the ABRSM aural tests. Because all aspects of musical training are of course connected, the student will also be singing, clapping, playing their instrument, writing music down, improvising and composing – as well as developing that vital ability to do well at the aural test in grade exams!

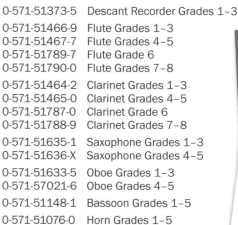

0-571-53438-4 Grade 1 (with CD)
0-571-53439-2 Grade 2 (with CD)
0-571-53544-5 Grade 3 (with CD)
0-571-53545-3 Grade 4 (with CD)
0-571-53546-1 Grade 5 (with CD)
0-571-53440-6 Grade 6 (with CD)
0-571-53441-4 Grades 7–8 (with CD)

Improve your practice!

Improve your practice! is the essential companion for pianists and instrumentalists, encapsulating Paul Harris's failsafe approach to learning. With boxes for filling in, make-your-own playing cards, a handy practice diary and an exam countdown, these books help to explore pieces and to understand their character. The books will enable the student to develop ways of getting the most out of their practice sessions – whatever their length. Most importantly, the wider musical skills such as aural, theory, sight-reading, improvisation and composition develop alongside, resulting in a more intelligent and all-round musician. Practice makes perfect!

0-571-52844-9	Piano Beginners
0-571-52261-0	Piano Grade 1
0-571-52262-9	Piano Grade 2
0-571-52263-7	Piano Grade 3
0-571-52264-5	Piano Grade 4
0-571-52265-3	Piano Grade 5
0-571-52271-8	Instrumental Grade 1
0-571-52272-6	Instrumental Grade 2
0-571-52273-4	Instrumental Grade 3
0-571-52274-2	Instrumental Grade 4
0-571-52275-0	Instrumental Grade 5

Improve your scales!

Paul Harris's *Improve your scales!* series is the only way to learn scales.

These workbooks contain not only the complete scales and arpeggios for the current ABRSM syllabus but also use finger fitness exercises, scale and arpeggio studies, key pieces and simple improvisations to help you play scales and arpeggios with real confidence.

This unique approach encourages the student to understand and play comfortably within in a key, thus helping them pick up those valuable extra marks in exams, as well as promoting a solid basis for the learning of repertoire and for sight-reading.

0-571-53411-2	Piano Grade 1
0-571-53412-0	Piano Grade 2
0-571-53413-9	Piano Grade 3
0-571-53414-7	Piano Grade 4
0-571-53415-5	Piano Grade 5
0-571-53701-4	Violin Grade 1
0-571-53702-2	Violin Grade 2
0-571-53703-0	Violin Grade 3
0-571-53704-9	Violin Grade 4
0-571-53705-7	Violin Grade 5
0-571-52024-3	Flute Grades 1–3
0-571-52025-1	Flute Grades 4–5
0-571-51475-8	Clarinet Grades 1–3
0-571-51476-6	Clarinet Grades 4–5

Improve your teaching!

Energising and inspirational, *Improve your teaching!* and *Teaching Beginners* are 'must have' handbooks for all instrumental and singing teachers. Packed full of comprehensive advice and practical strategies, they offer creative yet accessible solutions to the challenges faced in music education.

Group Music Teaching in Practice is a major resource designed to help class teachers, instrumental teachers and music services collaborate and refine their skills to enable them to deliver an holistic primary music curriculum.

These insightful volumes are distilled from years of personal experience and research. In his approachable style, Paul Harris outlines his innovative strategy of 'simultaneous learning' as well as offering advice on lesson preparation, aural and memory work, effective practice and more.

0-571-52534-2   Improve your teaching!
0-571-53175-X   Improve your teaching! Teaching beginners
0-571-53319-1   Group Music Teaching in Practice (with ECD)

The Virtuoso Teacher

By considering *The Virtuoso Teacher* and how a teacher might attain virtuoso status, renowned educator and writer Paul Harris delves into the core issues of being a teacher and the teaching process. A fascinating look at topics such as self-awareness and the importance of emotional intelligence; getting the best out of pupils; dealing with challenging pupils; asking the right questions; creating a master-plan; taking the stress out of learning and teaching for the right reasons. This seminal book is an inspirational read for all music teachers, encouraging everyone to consider themselves in a new and uplifted light, and transform their teaching.

0-571-53676-X
The Virtuoso Teacher

The Simultaneous Learning Practice Map Pad

A revolutionary way to set up practice. Take a piece to be practised and write its title in the box; add words to describe the character of the piece underneath. Then set about filling in the significant features in the appropriate bubbles and begin working through these, drawing lines to make connections between them as you go along. You will achieve some really effective Simultaneous Practice!

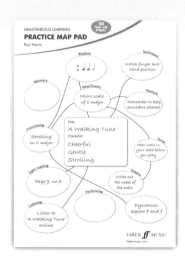

0-571-59731-9
The Simultaneous Learning Practice Map Pad

Faber Music Ltd.
Burnt Mill
Elizabeth Way
Harlow
Essex
CM20 2HX

t   +44 (0)1279 828982
f   +44 (0)1279 828983
e   sales@fabermusic.com
w   www.fabermusicstore.com
    @fabermusic
    facebook.com/fabermusic

Stage 4

Rhythmic exercises

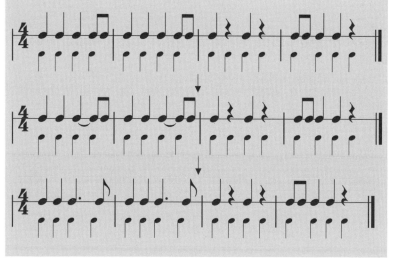
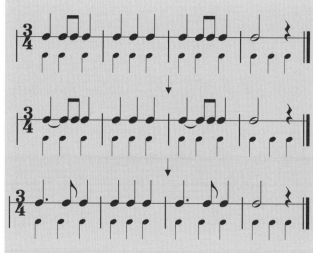

Melodic exercises

Set 1: Exploring ♩. ♪ in 4/4

1

2

Set 2: Exploring ♩. ♪ in 3/4

3

4

5

6

Prepared pieces

> **1** What is the key of this piece? Play the scale and arpeggio.
>
> **2** How many scale or arpeggio patterns can you find?
>
> **3** Does the rhythm in bar 1 appear again? Hear bars 1 and 2 in your head whilst tapping the pulse.
>
> **4** Now tap the pulse and think the rhythm of the whole piece. Then reverse, tapping the rhythm and thinking the pulse.
>
> **5** Play the first note and hear the piece through in your head, including musical expression.

1

> **1** In which key is this piece? Play the scale and arpeggio expressively. On which degree of the scale does the piece begin?
>
> **2** What do you notice about the first note of bars 1, 2, 3 and 4?
>
> **3** Think through the bowing.
>
> **4** Tap the pulse with one hand and the rhythm with the other. Repeat, swopping hands.
>
> **5** How will you put character into your performance?

2

Improvising

1

> Make up your own piece (it can be as long or as short as you like), beginning with this pattern. Keep the pulse steady. Decide on a mood or character before you begin.
>
>

2

> Now make up your own piece – including some dotted rhythms.

Going solo! Don't forget to prepare each piece carefully before you play it.

Stage 5

Staccato and pizzicato

Rhythmic exercises

Melodic exercises

Set 1: Exploring

Set 2: Exploring

Set 3: Exploring staccato and pizzicato

Prepared pieces

> **1** What is the key of this piece? Play the scale and arpeggio lightly.
>
> **2** Think carefully about the rhythm. Work at it in your favourite way.
> Are you sure you know how it goes?
>
> **3** Play the rhythm of the piece on an open string.
>
> **4** Now think about the bowing.
>
> **5** Play the first note and hear the piece through in your head, including musical expression.

> **1** In which key is this piece? Play the scale and arpeggio mysteriously.
>
> **2** How much of this piece is based on scale patterns?
>
> **3** Think through the fingering – especially in bars 3 and 5.
>
> **4** Tap the pulse with one hand and the rhythm with the other. Repeat, swopping hands.
>
> **5** How will you put character into your performance?

Improvising

> Make up your own piece (it can be as long or as short as you like), beginning with this pattern.
> Keep the pulse steady. Decide on a mood or character before you begin.

Going solo! Don't forget to prepare each piece carefully before you play it.

Stage 6

Rhythmic exercises

Melodic exercises

Set 1: Introducing simple ♪♪♪♪

Set 2: Two-note pairs ♪♪ ♪♪

Set 3: Exploring more ♪♪♪♪

Prepared pieces

> 1 Look through this piece. Do you feel you understand it?
>
> 2 Look carefully at the patterns: rhythmic and melodic. How much of it is based on the scale and arpeggio?
>
> 3 Play the scale *f* and arpeggio *mp*.
>
> 4 Now think carefully about the bowing.
>
> 5 Play the first note and hear the piece through in your head, including dynamics.

> 1 In which key is this piece? Play the scale and arpeggio *mf* then *mp*.
>
> 2 How many patterns can you find?
>
> 3 Think about the fingering in bars 1 and 6. What is interesting about these bars?
>
> 4 Tap the pulse with your hand and the rhythm with your foot. Then swop around.
>
> 5 How will you put character into your performance?

Improvising

> Make up your own piece (it can be as long or as short as you like), beginning with this pattern. Keep the pulse steady. Decide on a mood or character before you begin.

Going solo! Don't forget to prepare each piece carefully before you play it.

Stage 7

Rhythmic exercises

Melodic exercises

Set 1: Exploring

Set 2: Exploring

Prepared pieces

1 Play the scale and arpeggio loudly ascending and quietly descending.

2 To which pattern do the first three notes belong?

3 What will you count? Tap the pulse strongly and think through the rhythm.

4 Play the rhythm of the piece on the open D string.

5 Play the first note and hear the piece through in your head, including dynamics.

Spirito

1 In which key is this piece? Play the scale using rhythms from the piece.

2 How many repeated ideas can you find?

3 Set a pulse going in your head and hear the piece through in your head.

4 Study the first bar for a moment then play it from memory.

5 How will you put character into your performance?

Solemn

Improvising

Make up your own piece (it can be as long or as short as you like), beginning with this pattern. Keep the pulse steady. Decide on a mood or character before you begin.

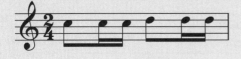

Going solo! Don't forget to prepare each piece carefully before you play it.